English
Activity Book

for ages 10-11

This CGP book is bursting with fun activities to build up children's skills and confidence.

It's ideal for extra practice to reinforce what they're learning in primary school. Enjoy!

Published by CGP

Editors:
Keith Blackhall, Emma Cleasby, Alex Fairer, Becca Lakin,
Hannah Roscoe and James Summersgill

With thanks to Alison Griffin and Catherine Heygate for the proofreading.

With thanks to Lottie Edwards for the copyright research.

ISBN: 978 1 78908 737 6

Printed by Elanders Ltd, Newcastle upon Tyne.
Clipart on the cover and throughout the book from Corel®
Cover design concept by emc design ltd.

Contents

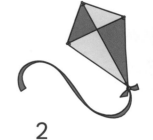

Word types

Nouns are naming words. Adjectives describe nouns or noun phrases. Verbs are doing or being words. Adverbs can describe verbs, adjectives or other adverbs.

The talented ballerina danced gracefully on the stage.

    ↑   ↑   ↑   ↑

adjective   noun   verb   adverb

Pronouns usually replace nouns in a sentence.

Rahima is happy because she adopted a new pet. ← 'she' replaces the proper noun 'Rahima'.

Determiners are small words that go before a noun to tell you more about it.

I want a cat.   I held the cat.   She has three cats.   That is his cat.

The cat has an orange tail.   Here are some cats.   Look at these cats.

Prepositions show how things in a sentence are related to each other.

He is leaving at noon because of the snow.   His bag is in the car.

           ↑   ↑   ↑

This shows when   This explains why   This shows where
he is leaving.   he is leaving.   his bag is.

1. Underline the determiners in the sentences below.

    Can you see those elephants playing in the water?

    You should have some cereal for your breakfast.

    Ophelia stayed in this hotel when she visited her friend.

    Stephen has read every book on that bookcase.

2. Fill in each gap with a suitable determiner. Try to use a different determiner in each gap.

    I have .... biscuits in .... lunchbox today.

    Tom and .... sister made .... snowman and .... igloo.

3. Complete the sentences below using the pronouns in the box. You should only use each pronoun once.

| her | it | them | he | him | ours |

Floyd is scared of the frogs so Halima has to hide _them_ from _him_ .

Claudia is excited to see Jacob because _he_ always bakes cookies for _them_ .

Their boat was much larger than ...., but .... was also a lot slower.

4. Add a suitable preposition to each sentence below.

Ashley dived .... the sea to collect shells.

Luke can't play football .... his injury.

Chidike fell asleep .... his piano lesson.

5. Rewrite the sentences below, adding two adjectives and an adverb to each sentence.

The tortoise sleeps under the sofa.	Juana knitted socks for her friends.
....	....
....	....
....	....

An Extra Challenge

Each box should contain a noun, a verb, an adjective, an adverb and a preposition. Can you work out which word type is missing from each box?

really	river	mouldy	nervously	during
frightens	murky	carefully	fragile	played
Bruno	slowly	cleans	carried	music
because of	towards	Cassie	into	tranquil

Can you write a sentence for each box that includes the words in the box and an example of the word type that's missing?

Can you tick a box to determine how well you did on these pages?

3

Synonyms and antonyms

Words that have the same or a very similar meaning are called synonyms.

huge **and** massive   funny **and** amusing

Words that mean the opposite of each other are called antonyms.

asleep **and** awake   old **and** young

Synonyms and antonyms are always the same word type as each other.

bright **and** vibrant   slowly **and** quickly

These synonyms are both adjectives.   These antonyms are both adverbs.

Now Try These

1. Draw lines to match the pairs of synonyms and antonyms in the boxes below.

SYNONYMS	
considerate	bawl
triumph	coarse
rough	victory
instantly	thoughtful
sob	immediately

ANTONYMS	
bland	allow
honestly	deceitfully
advance	uncertain
forbid	retreat
confident	flavourful

2. Write down a synonym to replace each of the underlined words in the sentences below.

I <u>detest</u> sweetcorn — it tastes horrible.   ....

Owain heard the <u>strange</u> noise again.   ....

Lyra bought lots of <u>gifts</u> for her family.   ....

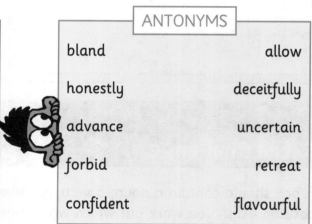

Rufus stomped <u>noisily</u> down the stairs.   ....

4

3. Underline the adjectives and adverbs in each sentence below. Then, rewrite each sentence, replacing the underlined words with antonyms so that each sentence means the opposite.

Teresa walked calmly past the friendly dog.

....

The furniture in the old-fashioned house was expensive.

....

I rarely eat the revolting carrots from the garden.

....

4. Write a sentence that uses a synonym of each word below.

puzzling   ⇨   ....

wise   ⇨   ....

journeyed   ⇨   ....

An Extra Challenge

Ksenia has written about her day in her diary, but she's included ten words that mean the opposite of what she meant to write.

Can you underline these words and then rewrite the entry, replacing the underlined words with antonyms so that the diary entry makes sense?

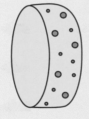

I woke up feeling refreshed after a terrible night's sleep. I bounded downstairs and ate my breakfast before leaving the house to meet Hugo at the park. The sun was dull and the birds were singing cheerfully. I wanted to take my favourite route along the river, but it was open while workers damaged the bridge. So I took the quieter route along the main road through town instead.

I waited in the park where we'd agreed, but Hugo was everywhere to be seen. Suddenly, I heard a loud whisper and saw two shapes getting smaller as they rolled down the hill towards me. Eventually, I realised that one shape was Hugo. The other seemed to be a tiny wheel of cheese that was avoiding him.

Did you find these pages easy or hard? Give a box a tick.

5

Homophones

How It Works

Homophones are words that sound the same, but have different meanings and spellings.

peak

A peak is the top
of a mountain.

peek

To peek means
to look quickly
or secretively.

Now Try These

1. Circle the word from each word pair that matches the definition.

   father / farther   coward / cowered   serial / cereal   principal / principle

   ⬇   ⬇   ⬇   ⬇

   a parent   crouched in fear   food made from grain   most important

2. Underline the mistake in each sentence below,
   then write the correct homophones on the dotted lines.

   Nicola's hoarse trotted along at a leisurely pace.   ➡ ....

   The lace bridle gown made her look like a princess.   ➡ ....

   My brother goes for a run every mourning.   ➡ ....

   You need a driving license to learn how to drive.   ➡ ....

   Penelope began her dissent down the spiral staircase.   ➡ ....

3. Can you write two homophones for each of the words below?

rowed	reign
.... , ...	.... , ...

4. Draw lines to match each sentence to the correct missing word.

You can buy the first ..... of our cookbook online.

Julian won a bronze ..... in the swimming race.

I never ..... in things that don't concern me.

Do you like the latest ..... to my antique collection?

edition

addition

medal

meddle

5. Write a sentence that uses both words in the box correctly.

allowed   ....

aloud   ....

throne   ....

thrown   ....

fought   ....

fort   ....

An Extra Challenge

Daniela has written a story, but her brother has sneakily replaced some of the words with their homophones. Can you find and correct the ten words that he's changed?

As Carl weighted by the sighed of the stage, he watched his friend Zahra oar the audience with her singing. The applause that erupted when she finished her song did nothing to lesson his nerves. He was next to perform. He could feel himself start to panic, but he took a deep breath as he'd been taut to. He new his song, and he could sing it well. It was thyme too prove to the whirled that his nerves wouldn't stop him from doing what he loved. He was going to sees this opportunity.

Are you a homophone hero?
Tick a box to show how you did.

Tricky words

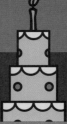

How It Works

There are some words that are tricky to spell. Here are some examples:

Some word endings sound similar but are spelt differently.

patience   entrance

visibly   probably

precious   ambitious

Some words ending in 'fer' change their spelling when you add a suffix. If the 'fer' is emphasised when you say the new word out loud, you need to double the 'r'.

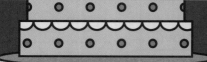

transfer + ing → transferring

'fer' is emphasised when you say this word out loud, so an extra 'r' is added.

Now Try These

1. Circle the correct spelling of each word to complete the sentences below.

There will be **torrencial / torrential** rain tomorrow.

The restaurant had **atrotious / atrocious** reviews.

The tale of the magic cat was probably **fictitious / ficticious**.

Regular exercise is **beneficial / benefitial** for your health.

2. Write the correct spelling of each word in bold on the dotted lines.

"That is a **marvelous** birthday cake," said Isla.   ➡ ....

There were several luxury **yots** in the harbour.   ➡ ....

Kevin tried to **pursuade** us to do his homework.   ➡ ....

Apparrently, a celebrity is coming to our school.   ➡ ....

The **semetry** was a very spooky place at night.   ➡ ....

3. Tick the words which will change their spelling when the suffix is added.

infer + ence ☐   prefer + ing ☐   suffer + er ☐

defer + al ☐   differ + ence ☐   confer + ed ☐

4. Use the clues below to complete the words which end in **-ance**, **-ence**, **-ancy** or **-ency**.

Clue	Word
a sweet, pleasant smell	fra....................
a situation where you need help	eme....................
the period when you're expecting a baby	pre....................
a lack of knowledge about something	ign....................
the result of something	cons....................
the type of money used in a country	cur....................
to see or feel something directly	exp....................

5. Fill in the missing letter in each word, then write a short paragraph that uses all the words.

ined.......ble   judgm........nt   remark.......bly   contest.......nt

....

....

....

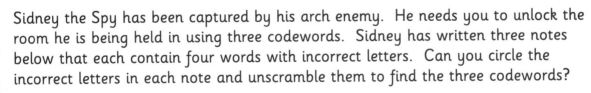

An Extra Challenge

Sidney the Spy has been captured by his arch enemy. He needs you to unlock the room he is being held in using three codewords. Sidney has written three notes below that each contain four words with incorrect letters. Can you circle the incorrect letters in each note and unscramble them to find the three codewords?

My arch enemy has been desperrate to catch me for months and now they've finally done it. Presumibly they plan to keep me locked up forever, but I am determinned to escape. Can I rely on you to find the secret codewords and rescue me? Reluctence is not an option.

Be suspitious of the guards — they definately cannot be trusted. I am, of course, refferring to the gnomes who patrol the courtyard. They can't resist a scrumpcious treat, so use cake to lure them away from the gate.

The room where I'm being kept is accessable via the control room — that's on the twelvth floor. There are many intriguing rooms near mine, but don't let curiocity get the better of you. I will be eternally grateful for your assistence.

Were these pages a trick or a treat? Give a box a tick.

Standard English

Standard English follows the normal spelling, punctuation and grammar rules.
You should always use Standard English in your written work.

✓ I don't like any vegetables.   ✗ I don't like no vegetables.

        ↑   ↑

    Standard English   Non-Standard English

✓ He's the man who has a dog.   ✗ He's the man what has a dog.

✓ She isn't coming to school.   ✗ She ain't coming to school.

Now Try These

1. Circle the sentences that use Standard English.

The dog was sitting in front of the fire.	She should of gone to sleep.	I sail around the world in my ship.
I is washing the dishes.	Ronald and I are quite tall.	It weren't me who broke the vase!
Can I see those pictures, please?	We've not got no new ideas.	Them red flowers are very pretty.

2. Circle the correct option so that each sentence is in Standard English.

We **seen / saw** a film about a giant shark on Sunday.

Anna and Theo **was / were** playing hide-and-seek.

I **went / gone** to a sausage dog race last weekend.

My friends have **came / come** to stay with me.

Have you **seen / saw** my guinea pig anywhere?

They **did / done** their chores before dinner.

3. Can you correct the text below so that it uses Standard English?

    After we ~~runned~~ ^{ran} through the park, we decided we was hungry. We

    went to a beautiful restaurant what served delicious soups and stews. I eaten the

    carrot and cabbage soup, and Mum had lentil stew. My soup was more nicer than

    Mum's stew. When we had finished, we didn't want nothing else to eat so we paid

    and gone home. Mum and me walked along the canal on the way back. We saw

    a grumpy-looking fisherman there — he must not of caught many fish that day.

4. Rewrite these sentences so that they use Standard English.

    Mrs Croft is learning us about Queen Victoria.

    ....

    Ekon jumped off of the diving board.

    ....

    My dad was jogging very slow.

    ....

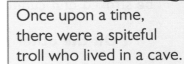

An Extra Challenge

Meg has written a short story about a troll, but the sentences aren't in the right order and each one uses non-Standard English. Can you rewrite the sentences in Standard English and put them in the right order to tell the story?

One day, a boy called Ade what lived in a nearby village decided he was gonna teach the troll a lesson.

When the troll come out, Ade throwed a net over him.

Once upon a time, there were a spiteful troll who lived in a cave.

The troll wouldn't let no one pass his cave.

Ade told the troll that he ain't releasing him until the troll promised to be less horrid.

Ade gone over to the troll's cave, called out to him and then hid.

Cohesive devices

You can use cohesive devices to link sentences and paragraphs together. Cohesive devices include repetition, adverbs and adverbials, and ellipsis.

Repeating the phrase 'the castle' helps to link these paragraphs together. → Karim hoped he would reach **the castle** before dawn. After hours of walking, **the castle** finally emerged from the mist. It towered menacingly above Karim.

Firstly, litter is a problem because it can injure wild animals and pets. **In addition**, littering makes areas look untidy and unclean. ← These two paragraphs are linked together using an adverb and an adverbial.

Ellipsis is where a word or phrase is removed. Here, 'buy milk' has been removed, which helps the sentence to flow. → Cheryl only buys milk when she needs to ~~buy milk~~.

Now Try These

1. Circle the best word or phrase from the brackets to link the paragraphs together.

There are many benefits to owning a dog, but there are also downsides.

(**First of all / In contrast**), you'll get regular exercise from walking your dog every day. Walking is an easy and enjoyable way to help you stay fit and active.

(**For example / Furthermore**), dogs are very affectionate pets — they love to be stroked and cuddled. Dogs form very strong and loving bonds with their owners.

(**On the other hand / Secondly**), taking care of a dog can be expensive. If your dog becomes ill, it can cost a lot of money to treat it at the vet.

(**However / Additionally**), you must pay someone to care for your dog if you go on holiday and can't take your dog with you.

(**Despite this / After all**), many people believe the advantages of owning a dog far outweigh the disadvantages.

2. Rewrite these sentences, removing the unnecessary words.

    a) I went for a bike ride because Mum told me to go for a bike ride.

    ....

    b) Darren made a cup of tea and he made a ham sandwich.

    ....

    c) Ross had a dessert after the meal, but Chloe didn't have a dessert.

    ....

3. Write the first sentence of the next paragraph in each story.
   Include one repeated word or phrase.

    a)   Silent as a mouse, Jenny tiptoed downstairs. Desperate to see her presents
            underneath the Christmas tree, she gently pushed open the living room door.

    ....

    ....

    b)   His chest pounding, Amir waited nervously for his teacher to announce the
            results. He hoped he'd done enough to be named Sports Day Champion.

    ....

    ....

An Extra Challenge

Can you write a story based on the storyboard below? Make sure you
use cohesive devices to link your sentences and paragraphs together.

   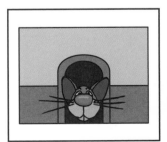

How strong are your
paragraph-linking skills?

Writing a formal text

How It Works

You should write in a formal way when you're writing for a serious reason, or to someone you don't know well. Formal texts should sound polite and impersonal.

You can make your writing formal by changing the vocabulary you use.

The thief fled. ← formal vocabulary   The thief did a runner. ← informal vocabulary

Formal texts don't use contractions.

We cannot speak here. ← You should say 'cannot' instead of 'can't'.

You can also use the subjunctive form to make your texts more formal. The subjunctive can be used to talk about things that could or should happen.

Had I been invited, I would have worn a bow tie.   If I were to attend, I would wear a bow tie.

This is more formal than 'If I had been invited'.   The subjunctive form uses 'were' instead of 'was'.

Now Try These

1. Underline the two informal words or phrases in each sentence below. Then, write a more formal alternative for each one on the dotted lines.

> My name is Mrs E. Dam and I am writing to say how gutted I am that you have decided to discontinue my fave flavour of biscuit.

....

> While I do get that cheese and caramel is quite an unconventional flavour combination, I reckon you would be surprised by just how versatile it can be.

....

> It upsets me that I am unable to get hold of them and will now have to find an alternative to scoff with my cheddar and onion tea.

....

2. Underline the contractions in the letter extract below,
   then write the full version of each contraction above it.

   would have

   I <u>would've</u> preferred it if there'd been some sort of announcement about the biscuits a

   few weeks ago. At least then I could've found a suitable replacement before you took

   them off the shelves. They're the tastiest biscuits I've ever had — I didn't think I'd ever

   need to consider other biscuit options, so I hope you'll understand why I'm so upset.

3. Tick the sentences below that use the subjunctive form.

   | If I were to visit my local supermarket now, I would cry. | ☐ |

   | I would reverse this terrible decision if I was in charge. | ☐ |

   | I would savour my last biscuit had I not already eaten it. | ☐ |

   | If you cared about your customers, you wouldn't do this. | ☐ |

4. Rewrite the sentence below so that it is more formal.

   If I'd known about this sooner, I wouldn't be so miffed.

   ....

   ....

An Extra Challenge

Imagine that you work for the biscuit company and you have just received Mrs Dam's letter.
Can you write a formal letter in reply to it? Use the prompts below to help you.

How do you think the company feels about Mrs Dam's letter?

Why did the company discontinue the biscuits?

What could the company do to make Mrs Dam feel better?

Did you come up with some
delicious answers? Tick a box.

 ☐ ☐ ☐

15

Writing an informal text

How It Works

Informal texts sound more friendly and chatty than formal texts.

I'll chill out for a bit because I'm shattered. ← informal vocabulary

Informal texts often use contractions.

He's brought you a present. ← This sentence uses 'He's' instead of 'He has'.

Informal writing sometimes uses question tags.

That's a lot of balloons, isn't it? ← The question tag 'isn't it' turns this sentence into a question.

Now Try These

1. For each pair of sentences, put a tick next to the informal version.

   a) I was gutted that we lost. ☐   I was disappointed that we lost. ☐

   b) The chef cooked a nice meal. ☐   The chef rustled up a nice meal. ☐

   c) She is a computer whizz. ☐   She is a computer expert. ☐

2. Read Olufemi's diary entry, then underline the words that make his text informal.

   <u>Saturday 8th March</u>

   Finally, it's the first day of half term! I've got heaps of stuff planned for today.

   First off, I'm meeting up with my pals from school for a natter. Apparently,

   Divya wants to tell us a bonkers story about something that happened to her sister

   yesterday evening. I really hope that she isn't winding us up like last time

   though. We were well annoyed when we found out that she was fibbing!

3. Read the next part of Olufemi's diary entry. Then, replace each bold word with a less formal word or phrase.

> I must **return** home by 3 o'clock because I'm going ➡ ....
> to the toy shop with my **father**. I've finally saved ➡ ....
> enough **money** to buy the robot I want. It can help ➡ ....
> me with my chores, record messages and do **lots** of ➡ ....
> other **brilliant** things. I can't wait to get it. ➡ ....

4. Rewrite the sentences below, using contractions where you can.

It will be so exciting to test the robot out. I have got so many chores it can do.

....

....

5. Rewrite the sentence below, adding a question tag to make it less formal.

The robot sounds really cool. ➡

....

....

An Extra Challenge

Olufemi has written diary entries for the next two days, but they use formal language. Can you rewrite his entries to make them less formal?

Sunday 9th March

I finally purchased my magnificent robot yesterday. I have named him Robert, which I think is a suitable name. He has already been remarkably useful. When my mother requested that I tidy my room this morning, Robert and I completed the task very promptly.

Monday 10th March

Unfortunately, it appears as though my parents have discovered how efficient Robert can be. They have given me many additional chores to ensure that I spend the same amount of time cleaning. This is most unjust.

Ticking a box to show how you got on is a fab idea, isn't it?

 ☐ ☐ ☐

A leafy foe

Mrs Peters has a problem — her greenhouse has been taken over by an evil plant who dreams of world domination. She needs to lock it up before it has a chance to escape, but she has lost the greenhouse key somewhere in her garden. Can you help her find it? Work out the answer to each question about the poem below to find eight letters. Then, unscramble the letters to reveal where the key is.

Mrs Peters was happily toiling away,
Under the rays of the burning sun.
Turning the dry dirt delicately,
With a rusty trowel caked in earth.
She **quenched** the wilting plants' thirst,
And watched the radiant blooms revive.

She strolled back and forth along the rows,
Admiring the endless sea of colour.
The sweeping lawn with its emerald blades
Embracing its **floral** neighbours with open arms.
Butterflies flitted between flowers,
And bees buzzed noisily while collecting **pollen**.

1. What type of poem is this?

   rhyming poem — J

   nonsense poem — T

   free verse — A

   limerick — S

3. Which line in the first verse contains alliteration?

   second — K

   third — H

   fourth — P

   sixth — A

2. How many of the **bold** words in the poem are adjectives?

   one — E

   two — B

   three — I

   four — C

4. The final line in the second verse contains...

   a metaphor — P

   personification — H

   a simile — C

   onomatopoeia — R

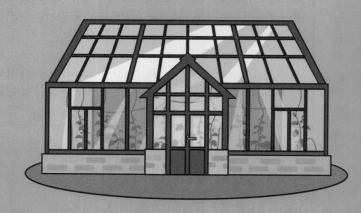

It only took a weak for the stem
To poke its head above the nutricious soil.
It quickly grew to a very grate height,
Its leafy vines invading every corner.
Then a giant flower bud gradually emerged,
As impressive as the rising sun.

But it wasn't long before she discovered
What this magnificent plant really was,
A mastermind so devilish and cunning
That it wanted to leave its glass house,
And wreak havoc on the outside world.
If only she hadn't saved that seed...

As she walked barefoot on the grass,
Something poked her naked heel.
A small brown seed with a green shoot,
Lying helplessly in the midday heat.
She placed it in a pot and gave it a drink,
And it immediately began to spread its roots.

6. Which verse contains a simile?

second — G

third — L

fourth — T

fifth — D

5. Which of these words is a synonym of 'spread' in the third verse?

unfurl — D

shrivel — U

shake — R

twist — W

8. Which of these words is an antonym of 'devilish' in the final verse?

beautiful — G

gentle — N

vicious — O

angelic — B

7. How many spelling mistakes are there in the fourth verse?

two — A

three — B

four — P

five — F

The key is in the...

Layout devices

Layout devices make informative writing clearer and more interesting.

· A heading tells you what the text is about.

· Subheadings split up big chunks of text.

· Bullet points break up the information in a list to make it easier to take in.

· Tables make some kinds of information easier to read.

heading ➙ **Menu**

subheading ➙ Starters

bullet points ➙
· tomato soup
· bread and olives
· salad

Destination	Glasgow	London	Leeds
Time of departure	09:30 am	10:00 am	11:00 am

← It's easier to read train times when they're in a table.

Now Try These

1. Read the text below. Complete the text by adding your own heading and subheadings.

[blank box]

[blank box]

We are thrilled to announce the grand reopening of the Southgate Hotel on 23rd May. The hotel has been closed for almost a year and we can't wait to welcome people back.

[blank box]

Following extensive renovations, all of our rooms are immaculately decorated and wonderfully comfortable — we guarantee you an excellent night's sleep.

[blank box]

We also now have a luxurious spa with a heated swimming pool, a sauna and a wide range of relaxing treatments. The spa is open to day visitors as well as hotel guests.

[blank box]

Our revamped restaurant promises a brilliant dining experience, offering an exciting menu of delicious cuisine made by our new award-winning chef and her team.

2. Rewrite the text below so that it uses bullet points.

There were many important developments in Britain during the Victorian era. For example, the postal system was greatly improved and the telephone was invented. The Victorian period also saw the expansion of the railway network. In addition, many people moved to towns and cities to find work.

....

....

....

....

....

....

....

3. Can you present the information from the paragraph below in the table?

Welcome to Emma's Ice Cream Parlour. Here are the prices of our ice creams — one scoop of ice cream costs £1.50, two scoops cost £2.50 and three scoops cost £3.00. All extra toppings are an extra fifty pence.

Scoops	1		
		£2.50	
		£0.50	

An Extra Challenge

Imagine a funfair is coming to where you live. Can you write a leaflet advertising the funfair? Take a look at the prompts below to help you plan and present your leaflet.

What are the main attractions going to be?

What food and drink will be available?

Use a heading to say what the leaflet is about.

Try to break up large chunks of text.

How could you show the opening times clearly?

Can you make any boring text look great? Tick a box.

Similes and metaphors

How It Works

Similes and metaphors are types of figurative language.
You can use them to make your writing more interesting.

A simile describes something by comparing it to something else.

> Megan's garden is like a jungle.
>
> The wind was as cold as ice.

Similes usually use the words 'like' or 'as'.

A metaphor describes something by saying it is something else.

> The tennis ball was a meteor tearing across the court.

Now Try These

1. Draw lines to show whether each sentence contains a simile, a metaphor or neither.

Like a fairytale prince, he was very charming.	simile
Mars is a planet that orbits the sun.	
I was a kettle of boiling anger.	metaphor
The ocean was as calm as a pond.	
The mountains are resting giants.	neither
Iqbal didn't think my joke was as funny as his.	

2. Turn the following similes into metaphors.

The drain gurgled like a strange monster.

....

Running around the track, Ngozi is as quick as a bolt of lightning.

....

3. Rewrite the sentence below using a simile. Then, rewrite it using a metaphor. Make
   sure the idea you use in your simile is different to the idea you use in your metaphor.

   The thunder was growing louder and louder.

   Simile: ....

   ....

   Metaphor: ....

   ....

4. Write a simile to describe picture a) and a metaphor to describe picture b).

   a)   b)

   ....

   ....

   ....

An Extra Challenge

Can you rewrite the text below to include three similes and three metaphors?

I strolled along the busy streets and gazed up at the towering
skyscrapers. People scurried along the pavements and
darted in and out of buildings. Occasionally, a police car
would drive past with its siren sounding, the traffic parting
to let it through. It was a grey day, but every now and again
the sun peeked through the clouds and lit up the city before
disappearing again. I continued walking and suddenly
emerged into a park which was calm and quiet. The neatly
trimmed grass was lovely and soft, and there was a large pond.

Do you know your similes from
your metaphors? Tick a box.

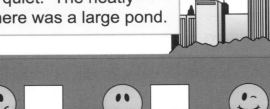

23

More figurative language

Onomatopoeia, personification and alliteration are also types of figurative language.

Onomatopoeia is where words sound like the thing they're describing.

> The pebble entered the water with a plop.

Personification uses human qualities to describe something that's not human.

> The heavy lorry crawled up the hill.

Alliteration is where words begin with the same sound.

> Kyle kindly made Kat a carrot cake. ⟵

Words don't have to start with the same letter to be alliterative — they just need to have the same sound.

Now Try These

1. Write down an onomatopoeic word to go with each scenario below. The first one has been done for you.

   | Hitting someone with a pillow | ➡ | ....thump.......... |

   | Walking in a muddy field | ➡ | .... |

   | Using the brakes on an old bicycle | ➡ | .... |

   | A woodpecker pecking a wall | ➡ | .... |

   | Frying eggs in a hot pan | ➡ | .... |

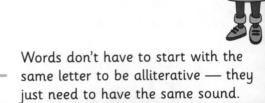

2. Replace the underlined words so that each sentence uses personification.

   The alarm clock <u>rang</u> noisily. ➡ ....

   The leaves <u>rustle</u> in the breeze. ➡ ....

   The shadows <u>moved</u> across the room. ➡ ....

   The floorboards <u>creak</u> as I walk over them. ➡ ....

3. Can you rewrite these sentences so that each one contains alliteration?

Freya caught a fish.

....

Dimitri made some doughnuts.

....

The cat was asleep.

....

4. Tick the two types of figurative language that are used in each sentence.

	Onomatopoeia	Personification	Alliteration
a) Moody Martin mumbled a mean comment as he left the room.	☐	☐	☐
b) Lara looked at the little moths dancing around the large light.	☐	☐	☐
c) The baby in the blue bonnet gurgled happily.	☐	☐	☐
d) The worn-out car protested angrily as I stomped hard on the accelerator.	☐	☐	☐

An Extra Challenge

Laura has written a story but she wants to use more figurative language.
Can you rewrite the text to include two examples each of onomatopoeia, personification and alliteration?

The wind blew through the trees as Ed looked out across the waters of Loch Ness. He desperately wanted to spot the famous monster that was believed to live there. Frustratingly, the only interesting thing he'd seen for hours was two crows sitting on a nearby wall. After a while, rain started to fall and he listened to it land on his coat. Reluctantly, Ed turned his back on the loch and walked over the gravel towards his car. Suddenly, he heard a noise behind him. He swung round and noticed a snake-like tail descend under the water.

Are you absolutely amazing at figurative language? Tick a box.

Types of writing

There are lots of different types of writing — they all have different purposes and features.

A biography is about someone else's life.

An autobiography is about the writer's own life.

Ken grew up in Newcastle with his three siblings.

I grew up in Newcastle with my three siblings.

Instructions tell you what to do.

Persuasion convinces you to do something.

Go for a walk every day to stay healthy.

Walking every day is an enjoyable and easy way to stay healthy.

Now Try These

1. Draw lines to match the book title to the type of writing it is.

How to Make Brownies

A Sporting Legend:
The Life of Jessica Mensah

My Adventures Growing Up

Why You Must Recycle

Biography

Persuasion

Instructions

Autobiography

2. Tick the features that each type of writing has.

Instructions

1. Butter the two slices of bread.
2. Place the cheese on one of the slices.

commands ☐
columns ☐
a list ☐

Persuasion

You need to buy these delicious crisps. They are the best crisps in the world!

facts ☐
second person ☐
exaggeration ☐

Autobiography

I began working for the charity in 1985. I was daunted at first but I loved helping people.

first person ☐
past tense ☐
third person ☐

Biography

During his sporting career, Graham won 20 tournaments. He retired in 2005.

third person ☐
facts ☐
rhetorical questions ☐

Read the text below about unicycles.

Children should all be given free unicycling lessons. They are spending too much time watching television, using the internet, or playing computer games. This disastrous trend cannot be allowed to continue. Children need regular exercise. They enjoy sports that are challenging and fun. No sport is more challenging or more fun than unicycling!

3. a) What type of writing is this? ....

    b) How can you tell?

    ....

    ....

4. Rewrite each sentence as the type of writing shown in the box next to it.

    I cycled to the lake and swam to the island. ➡ instructions

    ....

    ....

    Not much interested Ned, but he loved playing the guitar. ➡ autobiography

    ....

    ....

An Extra Challenge

Can you write an autobiographical text about an event in your life?
Take a look at the prompts below to help you plan and write your text.

Choose an interesting, funny or important event to write about.

Give your autobiographical text a title.

Explain what happened.

Include plenty of facts.

Write about how you felt.

How did it go? Which type of box are you going to tick?

Interviews

How It Works

An interview is a conversation made up of questions and answers.

The aim of an interview is usually to find out more information about a person or topic, or to ask for someone's point of view.

When did you decide that you wanted to become a guitarist?

It was soon after my eleventh birthday. My parents had bought me a guitar and I really enjoyed playing it. I started having lessons and I realised that it was the one thing I had a real talent for.

Here, the interviewer is asking for information.

The answer to the question helps us to learn more about the person being interviewed.

Now Try These

Read this interview with the manager of a museum.

Who discovered the fossil?

A member of the public stumbled upon it while they were walking their dog on the beach. They contacted the museum immediately and we sent someone down to take a look. We had no idea what to expect when we got there.

Is this a significant find?

It certainly is — this is a truly remarkable specimen. We have found small fragments of similar fossils in the past, which can currently be seen in the museum, but we have never come across anything in one piece like this before. Also, the level of detail preserved in the rock is unlike anything else we have on display.

What will this discovery mean for the museum?

First of all, this discovery will allow us to present a more complete picture of prehistoric life in this area. It is so important for people to learn about the history of the landscape around them. Secondly, I sincerely hope it will reinvigorate the public's interest in the museum's collections and help to boost donations. We really do rely on the public's ongoing support.

1. How does the manager feel about the discovery? How can you tell?

....

....

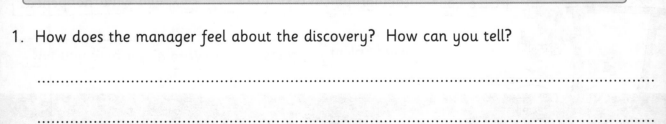

2. Give one reason why the fossil is more significant than others in the museum.

....

3. In your own words, explain the impact the fossil could have on the museum.

....

....

....

4. The interviewer asks the manager two more questions. Read the answers below and write down what you think the questions were.

....

> It is not uncommon to find them in this area. Our coastline is rich in fossils — the cliffs are made up of rocks which contain the remains of many different creatures.

....

> As the waves eat away at the cliffs, fragments of rock come tumbling down onto the beach and expose the fossils. It can take a long time for this to happen though.

5. Write down one more question you would ask the manager.

....

An Extra Challenge

> Imagine you've been asked to interview the person who found the fossil. Can you write down three questions to ask them? Then see if you can write down what you think their answers would be. Use the interview with the museum manager to help you.

Thanks for answering all my questions. How did you get on?

Poems

How It Works

Some poems have a rhyme scheme and a steady rhythm.

> Today I met a friendly Dalmatian,
> Waiting patiently at the train station.

Poems that don't have a rhyme scheme or a steady rhythm are called free verse.

> The werewolf's howl echoed all around,
> I felt the goosebumps travel up my arm.

Poems often use figurative language such as alliteration and similes.

> Gosia greedily gobbled up the grapes,
> She was as hungry as a pride of lions.

Now Try These

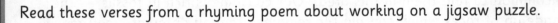

Read these verses from a rhyming poem about working on a jigsaw puzzle.

> The jigsaw puzzle was coming together,
> The perfect activity for horrid weather.
> With pieces scattered all over the table,
> We worked as quickly as we were able.
> The mountain of pieces was now just a hill,
> To finish so quickly would be such a thrill.
>
> Does this bit go here, or there? Maybe not...
> Their rightful homes could be so tricky to spot.
> But shapes soon emerged like the stars at night,
> Invisible at first, then beacons of light.
> The final picture was somewhere we had been,
> The perfect image of a wintry scene.

1. Why do you think the people in the poem are doing a jigsaw puzzle?

    ....

2. Find and copy a line from the poem that contains a simile.

    ....

3. Rewrite the final line of the poem using alliteration.

    ....

Now read these verses from a free verse poem about a snail.

I watched the delicate little snail
Leave a glistening silver line
Across the fallen autumn leaves.
They crunched under my foot,
But the tiny creature made no sound.

The sun was smiling down from high above,
Making the spiral patterns on its shell gleam.
Two tiny tentacles with beady eyes poked out,
Surveying the path which lay ahead.
It was a mighty journey for any snail.

4. Circle all the types of figurative language used in this poem.

alliteration   onomatopoeia   personification   simile

5. Complete the next verse of the poem with your own lines in free verse.

The shadowy depths of the bushes beckoned,
    But a ravenous blackbird swooped down
On the hunt for a satisfying morning snack...

....

....

6. Do you prefer rhyming poems or free verse poems? Can you explain why?

....

....

An Extra Challenge

Can you write the next two verses of the free verse poem below?
Make sure you write them in free verse and try to use figurative language.

We filled our water pistols to the brim,
    Ready for the afternoon battle.
    The shed was our mighty fortress,
    The bushes were our camouflage.
    Everyone was poised to begin the fight.
    I took a deep breath and gave the signal.

Are you a poetry prodigy, or
do you need more practice?

Playscripts

How It Works

Playscripts are stories that are written to be performed to an audience. They're usually split up into different scenes.

Before each scene, there's a short description of the setting.

Character names on the left show who is speaking. These names are always followed by a colon.

Brian and Geoff Danvers are in the living room. They've just discovered that the family hamster has escaped from its cage during the night.

BRIAN: *(frustrated)* How did she manage to get out? *(inspecting the door to the hamster cage)* The cage door is almost impossible for me to open, let alone a hamster.

(BRIAN stands with his hands on his hips, looking at the cage.)

Stage directions in brackets tell the actors how to perform their dialogue and what their character is doing. They're always written in the present tense.

GEOFF: *(determinedly, looking under the armchair)* Let's not worry about that right now, Brian. We need to find her before the kids come downstairs. They'll be so upset if they find out she's escaped.

(BRIAN sighs and nods, then starts looking under the furniture.)

Now Try These

1. Rewrite these sentences as stage directions. Remember to include brackets.

   Geoff spotted Cookie scurry behind the bookcase.

   Brian crawled silently across the room.

   ....

2. Can you rewrite these sentences as though they're part of a playscript? Don't forget to include the character names and stage directions.

   "She's over there," whispered Geoff, pointing.

   ....

   "There you are, Cookie," said Brian calmly.

   ....

3. Fill in the gaps in the playscript with your own words.

> GEOFF: *(anxiously)* Try to get her from behind the bookcase Brian — I hope she's not stuck!
>
> (BRIAN ....)
>
> BRIAN: (...) OW! You little devil!
>
> *(Cookie runs across the floor. GEOFF chases after her and manages to catch her.)*
>
> ....: (..., *while gently stroking Cookie)*
>
> That's enough excitement for one day. You're officially grounded, young lady.
>
> BRIAN: *(relieved)* ....

4. Read the next part of the story, then rewrite it as a playscript.
   Make sure you include all the dialogue and suitable stage directions.

> "I need to talk to you, Talia," said Brian sternly. "Who was the last person to close the door on Cookie's cage last night?" Talia looked at her dad, a confused expression on her face.
>
> "I thought you were, Dad," she said hesitantly. "You fed her before we went to bed, remember?"

....

....

....

....

....

An Extra Challenge

The family bought Cookie from a pet shop in their town. Can you write a playscript about what happened? Think about all the details in the boxes below.

SCENE DESCRIPTION	DIALOGUE	STAGE DIRECTIONS
Who is there? Where is the action taking place? What is happening in the scene?	What do the characters say to each other?	How should the actors say their lines? How should their characters behave?

NARRATOR: How did you get on?
YOU: I'll tick a box to show you.

Making comparisons

How It Works

Sometimes you need to make comparisons within a text or between two different texts. You can compare things like characters, settings and language.

> Melody gasped as she saw her gigantic birthday cake on the counter. Her little sister was sulking in the corner of the room, annoyed that there was no special cake for her.

> Bella watched eagerly as Peter opened his present. A flurry of meows erupted from the box. She smiled widely as he lifted up the tiny kitten and giggled contentedly.

The characters react differently to the cake. Melody is excited, but her little sister is unhappy.

The characters react the same way towards the kitten. They are both delighted.

If you compare both texts, Melody's sister and Bella react differently when something nice happens to someone else.

Now Try These

Read this text about a sports race.

> After a few hours of competition, it was time for the final race of the morning. The scorching sun bathed the stadium in light. The crowd created a lively atmosphere, filling the arena with noise. As the TV screens announced the next event, the audience cheered wildly for the competitors, who walked out onto the track and took their places at the starting line.
>
> Gino paced back and forth, trying to calm himself. His hands were shaking and his mind was a bustling motorway of thought. What if he didn't have the energy to perform well today? In the lane next to him, he saw Yuri take a deep breath and glance anxiously at his rivals. On the other side of Yuri, Rylan was staring straight ahead. His eyes were fixed on the finish line. He knew he could run faster than everyone else, so all he had to do was stay focused. A smile spread across his face as he pictured himself on the winner's podium.

1. Circle the option that best describes how Gino feels about the race.

   | enthusiastic | confident | nervous | relaxed |

2. Do you think Rylan feels the same way as Gino? How can you tell this from the text?

   ....

   ....

   ....

Now read this text about a theatre production.

> Manisha peeked out from behind the curtain. The audience members were waiting quietly in their seats, switching off their phones and having hushed conversations. Manisha's stomach was a boat swaying on a choppy sea — she desperately didn't want to forget her lines.
>
> Looking behind her, Manisha could see Joanna confidently reciting her lines to herself in the mirror. She repeated them over and over, using different voices and facial expressions each time. This was her first big role and she wanted to give a convincing performance.
>
> Meanwhile, most of the other actors were scurrying around like mice, rushing to make their final preparations. The play began at 7.30 pm so there was only ten minutes to go. Manisha was relieved to see some other unsettled faces — at least she wasn't the only one.

3. Tick the technique which is used in both texts.

simile ☐   metaphor ☐   personification ☐

4. Circle the statements about the settings of the texts that are true.

| Both texts are set indoors. |

| One setting is loud, the other is quiet. |

| One text is set in modern times, the other is set hundreds of years ago. |

| There is an audience in both settings. |

| Both texts are set in the evening. |

5. Do Gino and Manisha have similar feelings in these two texts? How can you tell?

....

....

....

An Extra Challenge

Jeff wants to write a short story where you can compare the ways the characters feel and behave. He's made a very rough plan below.

> Story idea: Three friends are playing hide-and-seek in the woods when they find an old treehouse.
>
> Characters: Carla and Mateo react in the same way to the treehouse, but Phoebe reacts differently.

Can you write a short story using this plan? Then see if you can summarise the similarities and differences between how your characters feel and behave.

How are your comparison skills shaping up? Tick a box.

  ☐   ☐   ☐

Answers

Pages 2-3 — Word types

1. Can you see <u>those</u> elephants playing in <u>the</u> water?
You should have <u>some</u> cereal for <u>your</u> breakfast.
Ophelia stayed in <u>this</u> hotel when she visited <u>her</u> friend.
Stephen has read <u>every</u> book on <u>that</u> bookcase.

2. Any sensible determiners that complete the sentences, e.g.
I have <u>two</u> biscuits in <u>my</u> lunchbox today.
Tom and <u>his</u> sister made <u>a</u> snowman and <u>an</u> igloo.

3. Floyd is scared of the frogs so Halima has to hide <u>them</u> from <u>him</u>.
Claudia is excited to see Jacob because <u>he</u> always bakes cookies for <u>her</u>.
Their boat was much larger than <u>ours</u>, but <u>it</u> was also a lot slower.

4. Any sensible prepositions, e.g. Ashley dived <u>into</u> the sea to collect shells. / Luke can't play football <u>because of</u> his injury. / Chidike fell asleep <u>during</u> his piano lesson.

5. Any sensible sentences, e.g. The tiny tortoise sleeps soundly under the leather sofa. / Yesterday, Juana knitted yellow socks for her grateful friends.

An Extra Challenge

The missing word types are: adjective / verb / preposition / noun / adverb.

Any sensible sentence for each box. Each sentence should use the words from the box and an example of the missing word type.

Pages 4-5 — Synonyms and antonyms

1. Synonyms: considerate — thoughtful / triumph — victory / rough — coarse / instantly — immediately / sob — bawl
Antonyms: bland — flavourful / honestly — deceitfully / advance — retreat / forbid — allow / confident — uncertain

2. Any sensible synonyms, e.g. hate, weird, presents, loudly

3. Teresa walked <u>calmly</u> past the <u>friendly</u> dog. — Teresa walked nervously past the aggressive dog. / The furniture in the <u>old-fashioned</u> house was <u>expensive</u>. — The furniture in the modern house was cheap. / I <u>rarely</u> eat the <u>revolting</u> carrots from the garden. — I often eat the delicious carrots from the garden.

4. Any sensible sentences, e.g. The instructions were <u>confusing</u>. / His grandparents were very <u>intelligent</u>. / She <u>travelled</u> through Europe last year.

An Extra Challenge

The words you should have underlined are: terrible, dull, open, damaged, quieter, everywhere, whisper, smaller, tiny, avoiding. You should have replaced these words with antonyms that make sense in the diary entry.

Pages 6-7 — Homophones

1. You should have circled: father, cowered, cereal, principal

2. Nicola's <u>hoarse</u> trotted along at a leisurely pace. — horse
The lace <u>bridle</u> gown made her look like a princess. — bridal
My brother goes for a run every <u>mourning</u>. — morning
You need a driving <u>license</u> to learn how to drive. — licence
Penelope began her <u>dissent</u> down the spiral staircase. — descent

3. rowed — road, rode / reign — rein, rain

4. You can buy the first <u>edition</u> of our cookbook online.

Julian won a bronze <u>medal</u> in the swimming race.
I never <u>meddle</u> in things that don't concern me.
Do you like the latest <u>addition</u> to my antique collection?

5. Any sensible sentences, e.g. We aren't allowed to read aloud in the library. / The jester was thrown out of the throne room. / They fought to regain control of the fort.

An Extra Challenge

The homophones you should have found and corrected are: weighted (waited), sighed (side), oar (awe), lesson (lessen), taut (taught), new (knew), thyme (time), too (to), whirled (world), sees (seize).

Pages 8-9 — Tricky words

1. You should have circled: torrential, atrocious, fictitious, beneficial.

2. marvellous, yachts, persuade, Apparently, cemetery

3. You should have ticked: defer + al / prefer + ing / confer + ed.

4. frag<u>r</u>ance, emerge<u>n</u>cy, preg<u>n</u>ancy, ig<u>n</u>orance, cons<u>e</u>quence, curr<u>en</u>cy, exp<u>e</u>rience

5. inedible, judgment, remarkably, contest<u>a</u>nt
Any sensible paragraph that uses all the words, e.g.
One contestant cooked a remarkably tasty steak. The other competitors made inedible dishes and waited nervously for my judgement.

An Extra Challenge

First note: desperrate, Presumibly, determinned, Reluctance — codeword: rein. Second note: suspitious, definately, refferring, scrumpcious — codeword: fact. Third note: accessable, twelvth, curiocity, assistence — codeword: cave.

Pages 10-11 — Standard English

1. You should have circled: The dog was sitting in front of the fire. / I sail around the world in my ship. / Ronald and I are quite tall. / Can I see those pictures, please?

2. We <u>saw</u> a film about a giant shark on Sunday.
Anna and Theo <u>were</u> playing hide-and-seek.
I <u>went</u> to a sausage dog race last weekend.
My friends have <u>come</u> to stay with me.
Have you <u>seen</u> my guinea pig anywhere?
They <u>did</u> their chores before dinner.

3. Any sensible corrections, e.g. After we ran through the park, we decided we <u>were</u> hungry. We went to a beautiful restaurant <u>that</u> served delicious soups and stews. I <u>ate</u> the carrot and cabbage soup, and Mum had lentil stew. My soup <u>was nicer</u> than Mum's stew. When we had finished, we didn't want <u>anything</u> else to eat so we paid and <u>went</u> home. Mum and <u>I</u> walked along the canal on the way back. We saw a grumpy-looking fisherman there — he must not <u>have</u> caught many fish that day.

4. Mrs Croft is teaching us about Queen Victoria. / Ekon jumped off the diving board. / My dad was jogging very slowly.

An Extra Challenge

Once upon a time, there <u>was</u> a spiteful troll who lived in a cave. The troll wouldn't let <u>anyone</u> pass his cave. One day, a boy called Ade <u>who</u> lived in a nearby village decided he was <u>going to</u> teach the troll a lesson. Ade <u>went</u> over to the troll's cave, called out to him and then hid. When the troll <u>came</u> out, Ade <u>threw</u> a net over him. Ade <u>told</u> the troll that he <u>wouldn't release</u> him until the troll promised to be less horrid.

Answers

Pages 12-13 — Cohesive devices

1. You should have circled: First of all / Furthermore / On the other hand / Additionally / Despite this

2. a) I went for a bike ride because Mum told me to.
   b) Darren made a cup of tea and a ham sandwich.
   c) Ross had a dessert after the meal, but Chloe didn't.

3. Any sensible sentence that uses one repeated word or phrase from the previous paragraph, e.g.
   a) At the opposite end of the room, the Christmas tree stood with its lights gently twinkling in the dark.
   b) "I'm pleased to announce that this year's Sports Day Champion is Amir. Congratulations!"

   An Extra Challenge

   Any sensible story based on the storyboard that uses cohesive devices to link sentences and paragraphs.

Pages 14-15 — Writing a formal text

1. <u>gutted</u>, <u>fave</u> — e.g. devastated, favourite / <u>get</u>, <u>reckon</u> — e.g. understand, believe / <u>get hold of</u>, <u>scoff</u> — e.g. obtain, eat

2. You should have underlined: there'd (there had) / could've (could have) / They're (They are) / I've (I have) / didn't (did not) / I'd (I would) / you'll (you will) / I'm (I am)

3. You should have ticked: If I were to visit my local supermarket now, I would cry. / I would savour my last biscuit had I not already eaten it.

4. Any sensible sentence that is more formal, e.g. Had I known about this sooner, I would not be so disgruntled.

   An Extra Challenge

   Any sensible formal letter.

Pages 16-17 — Writing an informal text

1. You should have ticked:
   a) I was gutted that we lost.
   b) The chef rustled up a nice meal.
   c) She is a computer whizz.

2. You should have underlined: heaps of stuff / First off / pals / natter / bonkers / winding us up / well / fibbing
   You could also have underlined examples of contractions: it's / I've / I'm / isn't

3. Any sensible less formal words or phrases, e.g. get / dad / cash / loads / wicked

4. It'll be so exciting to test the robot out. I've got so many chores it can do.

5. Any sensible question tag, e.g. The robot sounds really cool, doesn't it?

   An Extra Challenge

   Any sensible rewrite of the diary entries to make them less formal.

Pages 18-19 — A leafy foe

1. free verse — A

2. three — I ('floral', 'naked' and 'cunning' are adjectives. 'quenched' and 'invading' are verbs, 'pollen' is a noun, and 'helplessly' is an adverb.)

3. third — H ('Turning the <u>dry</u> <u>dirt</u> delicately')

4. onomatopoeia — R ('buzzed' is an example of onomatopoeia.)

5. unfurl — D

6. fourth — T ('Then a giant flower bud gradually emerged, / As impressive as the rising sun')

7. three — B (weak — week, nutricious — nutritious, grate — great)

8. angelic — B
   The key is in the BIRDBATH.

Pages 20-21 — Layout devices

1. Any sensible answers, e.g. Southgate Hotel Reopens!, Reopening on 23rd May, Sleep Well in Our Rooms, Relax in the Spa, Visit Our Top-Quality Restaurant

2. There were many important developments in Britain during the Victorian era:
   · The postal system was greatly improved.
   · The telephone was invented.
   · The railway network was expanded.
   · Many people moved to towns and cities to find work.

3.

Scoops	1	2	3
Price	£1.50	£2.50	£3.00
Extra Toppings	£0.50		

   An Extra Challenge

   Any sensible leaflet that uses layout devices effectively.

Pages 22-23 — Similes and metaphors

1. Like a fairytale prince, he was very charming. — simile / Mars is a planet that orbits the sun. — neither / I was a kettle of boiling anger. — metaphor / The ocean was as calm as a pond. — simile / The mountains are resting giants. — metaphor / Iqbal didn't think my joke was as funny as his. — neither

2. Any sensible answers, e.g. The drain was a strange, gurgling monster. / Ngozi is a bolt of lightning running around the track.

3. Any sensible answers, e.g. The thunder was like a roaring lion, growing louder and louder. / The thunder was a booming cannon, growing louder and louder.

4. Any sensible answers, e.g.
   a) She skied down the hill as fast as an avalanche.
   b) The flames were fingers tickling the air.

   An Extra Challenge

   Any sensible rewriting of the text so that there are three similes and three metaphors.

Pages 24-25 — More figurative language

1. Any sensible answers, e.g. squelch / screech / knock / splutter.

2. Any sensible answers, e.g. screamed / chatter / crept / complain

3. Any sensible answers, e.g.
   Freya finally caught a fresh fish.
   Dimitri made some delicious doughnuts for dessert.
   The cuddly cat was curled up asleep in the corner.

4. a) onomatopoeia and alliteration
   b) personification and alliteration
   c) onomatopoeia and alliteration
   d) onomatopoeia and personification

Answers

An Extra Challenge

Any sensible rewriting of the text so that there are two examples each of onomatopoeia, personification and alliteration.

Pages 26-27 — Types of writing

1. How to Make Brownies — Instructions
   A Sporting Legend: The Life of Jessica Mensah — Biography
   My Adventures Growing Up — Autobiography
   Why You Must Recycle — Persuasion

2. Instructions — commands, a list / Persuasion — second person, exaggeration / Autobiography — first person, past tense / Biography — third person, facts

3. a) Persuasion
   b) Any sensible answer, e.g. The text uses exaggeration to try and convince the reader that unicycling is a great sport and that children should be given free unicycling lessons.

4. Any sensible answers, e.g. Cycle to the lake. Then, swim to the island. / Not much interested me, but I loved playing the guitar.

An Extra Challenge

Any sensible autobiographical text.

Pages 28-29 — Interviews

1. Any sensible answer, e.g. The manager feels pleased about the discovery because they describe the fossil as 'remarkable'.

2. Any one of the following: It's in one piece. / There is a lot of detail preserved in the rock.

3. Any sensible answer, e.g. It will help the museum teach people more about the history of the area. It could also make people more interested in the museum and encourage them to support it.

4. Any sensible questions, e.g. Is it unusual to find fossils in this area? / How do the fossils end up on the beach?

5. Any sensible question, e.g. Have you ever found a fossil yourself?

An Extra Challenge

Any three sensible questions and answers.

Pages 30-31 — Poems

1. Because the weather outside is horrible.

2. But shapes soon emerged like the stars at night

3. Any sensible answer, e.g. The perfect picture of a snowy scene.

4. You should have circled: alliteration ('Two tiny tentacles'), onomatopoeia ('They crunched under my foot') and personification ('The sun was smiling down from high above').

5. Any sensible lines that complete the next verse of the poem, e.g. I darted forward as fast as an arrow. /
   And with a disappointed squawk, the bird fled.

6. Any sensible answer, e.g. I prefer rhyming poems because I like the sound that rhyming words make. OR e.g. I prefer free verse poems. I think the language is more interesting because poets aren't forced to use words that rhyme.

An Extra Challenge

Any sensible continuation of the poem in free verse.

Pages 32-33 — Playscripts

1. Any sensible answers, e.g.
   (GEOFF spots Cookie scurry behind the bookcase.)
   (BRIAN crawls silently across the room.)

2. Any sensible answers, e.g.
   GEOFF: (whispering and pointing) She's over there.
   BRIAN: (calmly) There you are, Cookie.

3. Any sensible answers that make sense in the playscript, e.g.
   (BRIAN carefully reaches behind the bookcase.) / (shouting in pain) / GEOFF / (chuckling, while gently stroking Cookie) / Thank goodness you managed to catch her.

4. Any sensible answer, e.g.
   BRIAN: (sternly) I need to talk to you, Talia. Who was the last person to close the door on Cookie's cage last night?
   (TALIA looks at BRIAN, a confused expression on her face.)
   TALIA: (hesitantly) I thought you were, Dad. You fed her before we went to bed, remember?

An Extra Challenge

Any sensible playscript that includes a scene description, dialogue and stage directions.

Pages 34-35 — Making comparisons

1. You should have circled: nervous.

2. Any sensible answer, e.g. No, because Rylan is described as calm and confident. He looks 'straight ahead' and pictures himself winning the race.

3. You should have ticked: metaphor ('his mind was a bustling motorway of thought' and 'Manisha's stomach was a boat swaying on a choppy sea').

4. You should have circled: There is an audience in both settings. / One setting is loud, the other is quiet.

5. Any sensible answer, e.g. Yes. Gino and Manisha both feel nervous about something they're going to do. Gino's hands are 'shaking' and Manisha's stomach is 'a boat swaying on a choppy sea'.

An Extra Challenge

Any sensible short story that uses Jeff's rough plan.

Any sensible summary of the similarities and differences between how the characters feel and behave in the story.

EPF6O21